KU-200-400

CONTENTS

Spider-Man Vintage Annual is published under license by Panini Publishing, a division of PANINI UK LTD.
Office of publication: Panini UK Ltd., Brockbourne House, 77 Mount Ephraim, Tunbridge Wells, Kent, TN4 8BS.
This publication may not be sold, except by authorised dealers, and is sold subject to the condition that it shall not be sold or distributed with any part of its cover or markings removed, nor in a mutilated condition. Printed in Italy.
ISBN: 978-1-84653-171-2

MARVEL

marvel.com

TM & © 2012 Marvel & Subs.

HI, WEB-SLINGERS!

WOW! I CAN'T BELIEVE THAT YOUR FRIENDLY NEIGHBOURHOOD SPIDER-MAN IS FIFTY-YEARS OLD! WHO WOULD HAVE THOUGHT THAT THE CHARACTER OF A SCRAWNY TEENAGER WITH SPIDER-POWERS AND AN AILING AUNT, CREATED BY YOURS TRULY AND ARTIST STEVE DITKO, WOULD BECOME THE WORLD'S FAVOURITE SUPERHERO!

SO WHAT BETTER WAY TO CELEBRATE SPIDEY'S FIVE DECADES AT THE TOP THAN WITH THIS FINE TOME SHOWCASING SOME OF HIS GREATEST, EARLY ADVENTURES?

BUT YOU'D BETTER HANG ON TIGHT, TRUE BELIEVERS! WITHIN THESE HALLOWED PAGES YOU WILL FIND NOT ONLY SPIDER-MAN'S ORIGIN AND VERY FIRST APPEARANCE, BUT ALSO HIS FIRST ADVENTURE AS HE TACKLES THE CUNNING CHAMELEON. THEN, BEFORE YOU CAN CATCH YOUR BREATH, SPIDEY TRAVELS TO THE FLORIDA EVERGLADES TO TRACK DOWN THE MYSTERIOUS MONSTER WHO IS TERRORIZING THE SWAMP - A MISSION THAT BRINGS THE WALL-CRAWLER INTO CONFLICT WITH ONE OF HIS MOST TRAGIC AND ENDURING FOES... THE LETHAL LIZARD!

WE ROUND OFF THIS PERFECT PACKAGE OF WEB-SWINGING WONDERMENT WITH A TALE PACKED FULL OF SO MUCH TENSION AND SUSPENSE THAT IT SHOULD COME WITH A HEALTH WARNING! SPIDER-MAN'S DEADLIEST FOES, DOCTOR OCTOPUS, THE SANDMAN, ELECTRO, THE VULTURE, CHAMELEON AND MYSTERIO, JOIN FORCES AS THE SINISTER SIX TO DESTROY THE WALL-CRAWLER ONCE AND FOR ALL!

AND AS IF THAT'S NOT ENOUGH, WE'VE PACKED THIS ASTOUNDING ANNUAL WITH LOADS OF FACT-FILES AND PIN-UPS!

NO, NO, DON'T BOTHER TRYING TO THANK US. JUST SIT BACK AND ENJOY THE READ.

EXCELSIOR!

STAN

Stan Lee

SINCE 62

£12.99

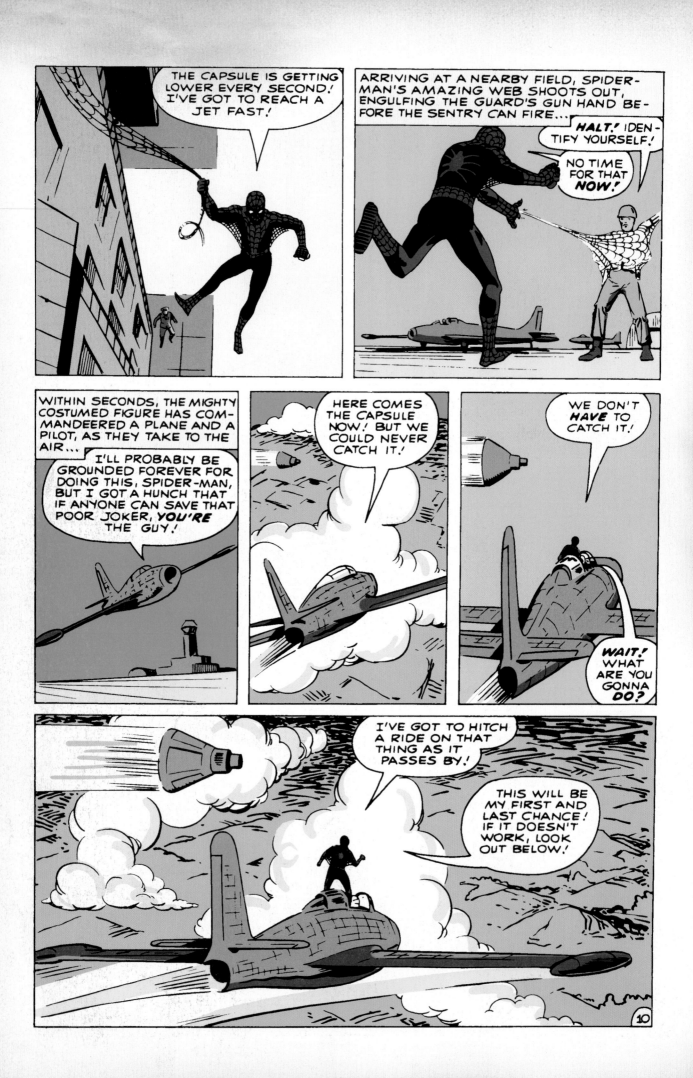

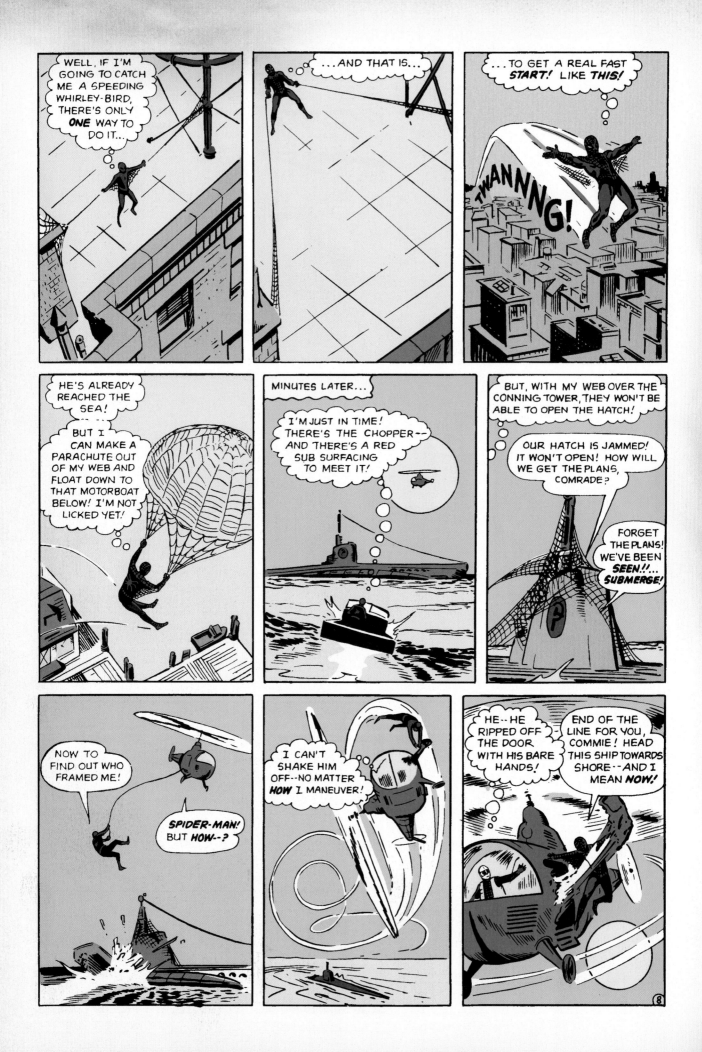

THE CHAMELEON

FIRST APPEARED IN...

the **AMAZING SPIDER-MAN**

1 MAR.

A NEW ERA IN COMICDOM WAS BORN WITH THE INTRODUCTION OF THE CHAMELEON! THE TITLE *"AMAZING FANTASY"* WAS CHANGED TO *"THE AMAZING SPIDER-MAN"*, AND SPIDEY FOUGHT HIS FIRST COLORFUL SUPER-FOE!

TO THIS DAY, NO ONE HAS EVER LEARNED THE TRUE IDENTITY OF THE MAN WHO CAN TRANSFORM HIMSELF INTO ANYBODY! SO SUCCESSFUL IS THE CHAMELEON'S POWER OF DISGUISE THAT HE ALMOST CONVINCED THE POLICE THAT HE WAS SPIDER-MAN DURING THEIR FIRST UNFORGETABLE ENCOUNTER!

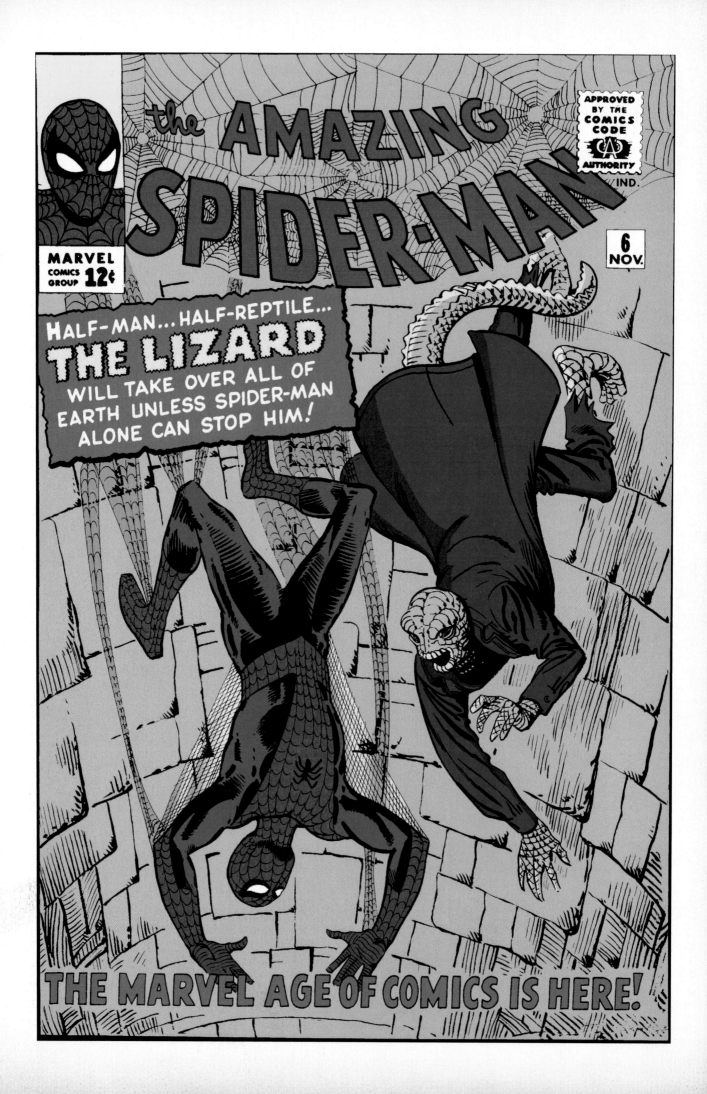

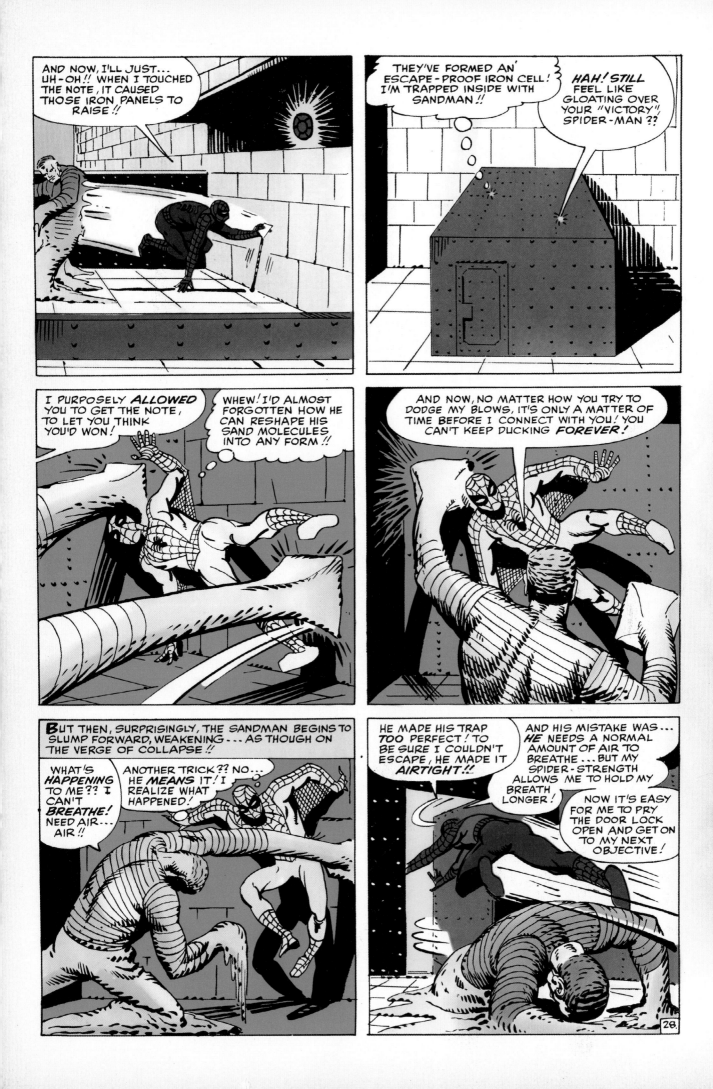

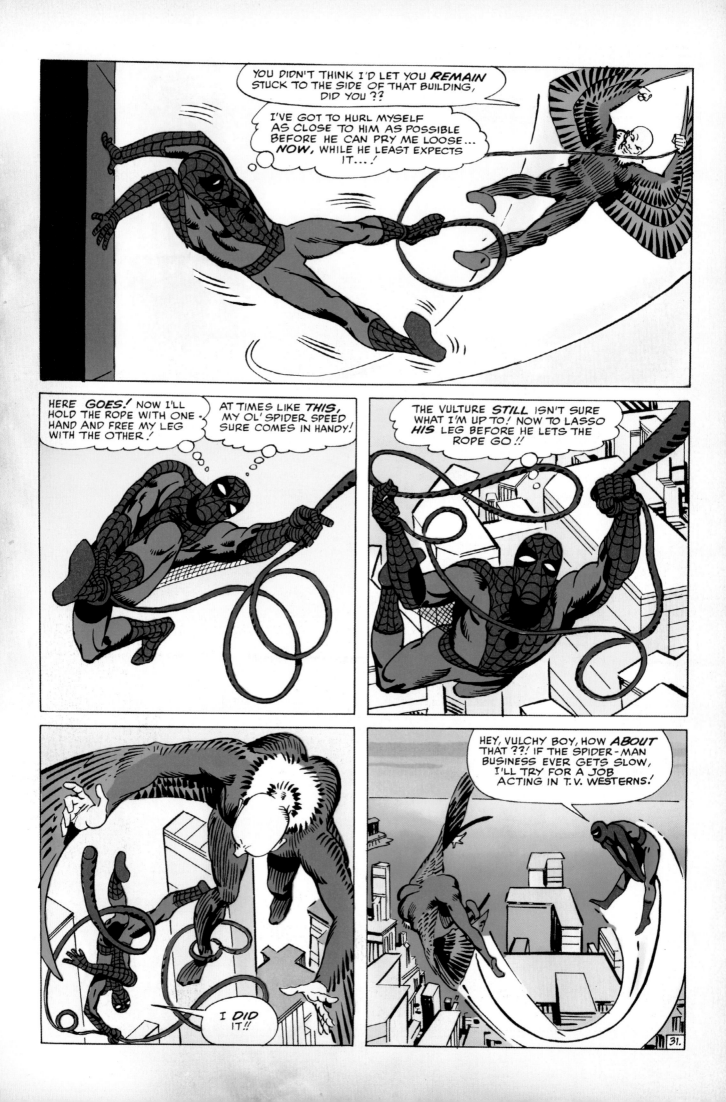

THE AMAZING, ALMOST LEGENDARY CAREER OF THE YOUTH KNOWN AS *SPIDER-MAN* HAD ITS BEGINNING SOME TIME AGO, IN THE SCIENCE HALL OF MIDTOWN HIGH SCHOOL, WHERE A DEMONSTRATION OF RADIO-ACTIVITY WAS TAKING PLACE...

NO ONE AT THE EXHIBITION NOTICED A TINY *SPIDER* DESCENDING ON A THIN STRAND OF WEB... A SPIDER WHICH FATE HAD CHOSEN TO ABSORB A FANTASTIC AMOUNT OF RADIOACTIVITY AT THE PRECISE MOMENT THAT PETER PARKER WALKED BY!

IN SUDDEN SHOCK, THE DYING INSECT BIT THE NEAREST LIVING THING A SPLIT-SECOND BEFORE THE LIFE FADED FROM FROM ITS BODY... AND, THAT NEAREST LIVING THING WAS THE LAD WHO WAS LATER TO BECOME THE WORLD'S MOST EXCITING TEEN-AGER!

A *SPIDER* JUST BIT ME!! BUT... WHY IS MY HAND *BURNING* SO?!

AS ALMOST EVERY MAGAZINE READER THROUGHOUT THE FREE WORLD KNOWS BY NOW, IT WAS THAT BITE WHICH SO AFFECTED THE CHEMICAL BALANCE IN PETER PARKER'S BLOOD, THAT IT CHANGED HIM INTO THE AMAZING *SPIDER-MAN!!*

AND NOW, LET US CAREFULLY EXAMINE THE POWERS WHICH PETER PARKER POSSESSES AS *SPIDER-MAN!*

LET US LEARN THE EXACT NUMBER AND EXTENT OF THEM, AS WE DISCUSS THE THINGS HE CAN, AND CANNOT DO...

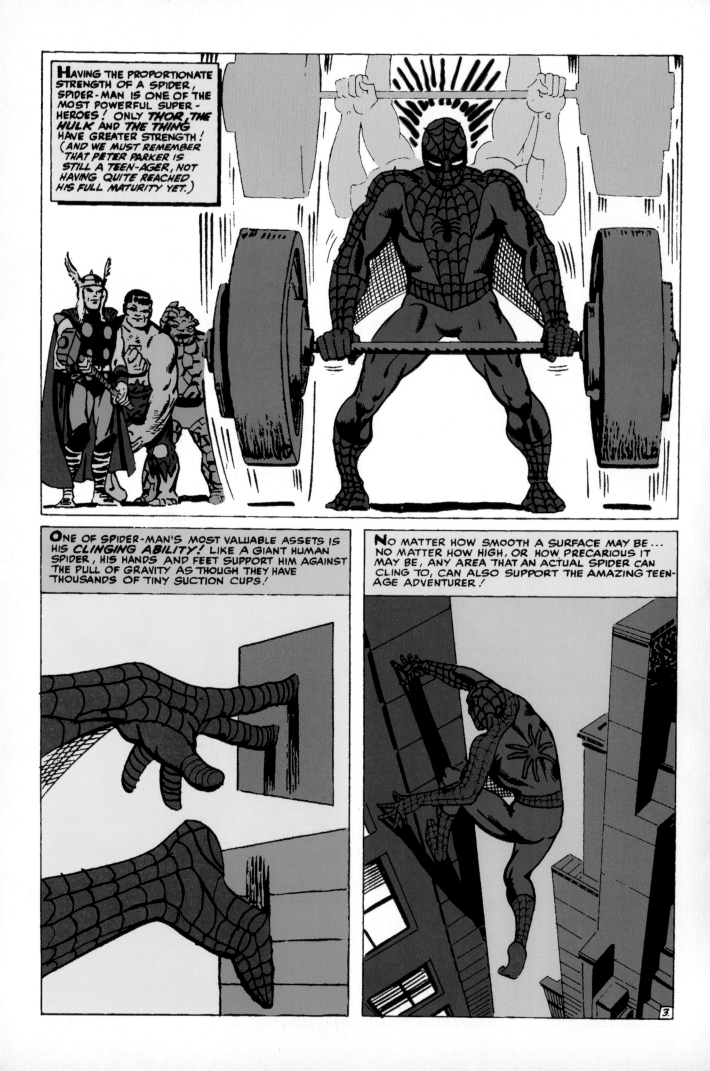

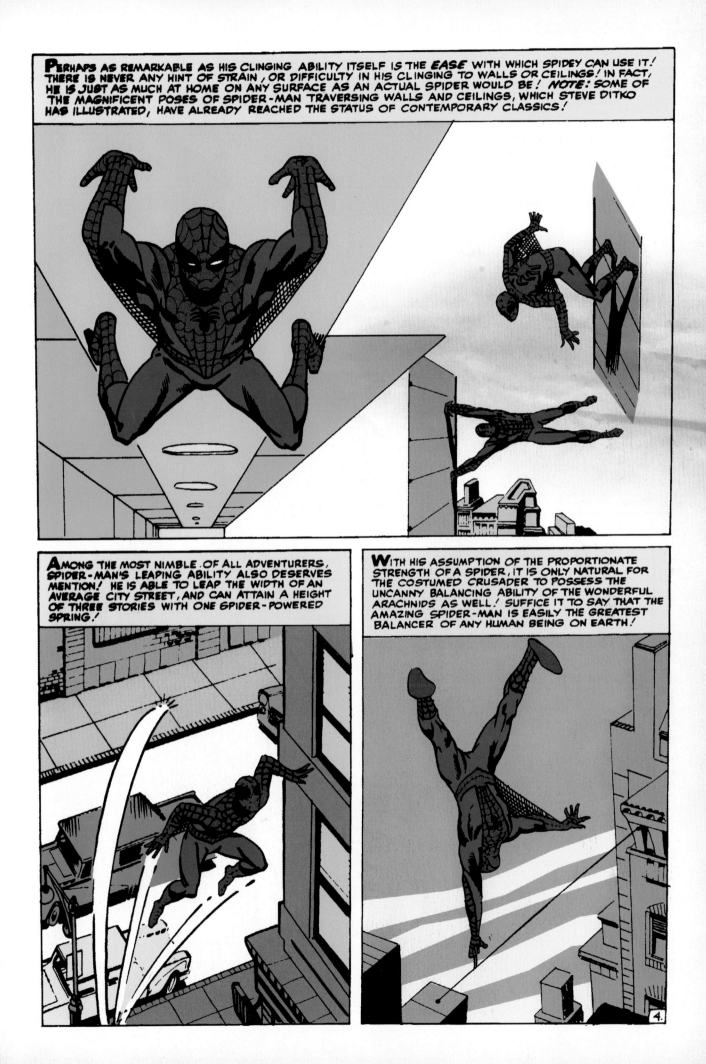

PERHAPS AS REMARKABLE AS HIS CLINGING ABILITY ITSELF IS THE *EASE* WITH WHICH SPIDEY CAN USE IT! THERE IS NEVER ANY HINT OF STRAIN, OR DIFFICULTY IN HIS CLINGING TO WALLS OR CEILINGS! IN FACT, HE IS JUST AS MUCH AT HOME ON ANY SURFACE AS AN ACTUAL SPIDER WOULD BE! *NOTE:* SOME OF THE MAGNIFICENT POSES OF SPIDER-MAN TRAVERSING WALLS AND CEILINGS, WHICH STEVE DITKO HAS ILLUSTRATED, HAVE ALREADY REACHED THE STATUS OF CONTEMPORARY CLASSICS!

AMONG THE MOST NIMBLE OF ALL ADVENTURERS, SPIDER-MAN'S LEAPING ABILITY ALSO DESERVES MENTION! HE IS ABLE TO LEAP THE WIDTH OF AN AVERAGE CITY STREET, AND CAN ATTAIN A HEIGHT OF THREE STORIES WITH ONE SPIDER-POWERED SPRING!

WITH HIS ASSUMPTION OF THE PROPORTIONATE STRENGTH OF A SPIDER, IT IS ONLY NATURAL FOR THE COSTUMED CRUSADER TO POSSESS THE UNCANNY BALANCING ABILITY OF THE WONDERFUL ARACHNIDS AS WELL! SUFFICE IT TO SAY THAT THE AMAZING SPIDER-MAN IS EASILY THE GREATEST BALANCER OF ANY HUMAN BEING ON EARTH!

4.

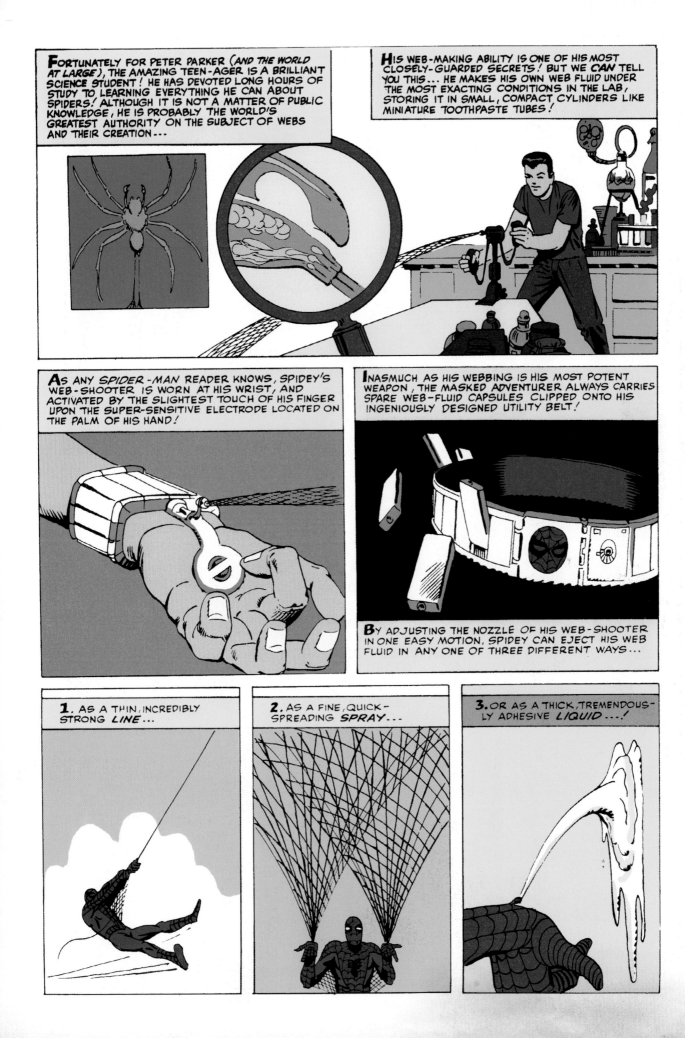

FORTUNATELY FOR PETER PARKER (AND THE WORLD AT LARGE), THE AMAZING TEEN-AGER IS A BRILLIANT SCIENCE STUDENT! HE HAS DEVOTED LONG HOURS OF STUDY TO LEARNING EVERYTHING HE CAN ABOUT SPIDERS! ALTHOUGH IT IS NOT A MATTER OF PUBLIC KNOWLEDGE, HE IS PROBABLY THE WORLD'S GREATEST AUTHORITY ON THE SUBJECT OF WEBS AND THEIR CREATION...

HIS WEB-MAKING ABILITY IS ONE OF HIS MOST CLOSELY-GUARDED SECRETS! BUT WE CAN TELL YOU THIS... HE MAKES HIS OWN WEB FLUID UNDER THE MOST EXACTING CONDITIONS IN THE LAB, STORING IT IN SMALL, COMPACT CYLINDERS LIKE MINIATURE TOOTHPASTE TUBES!

AS ANY SPIDER-MAN READER KNOWS, SPIDEY'S WEB-SHOOTER IS WORN AT HIS WRIST, AND ACTIVATED BY THE SLIGHTEST TOUCH OF HIS FINGER UPON THE SUPER-SENSITIVE ELECTRODE LOCATED ON THE PALM OF HIS HAND!

INASMUCH AS HIS WEBBING IS HIS MOST POTENT WEAPON, THE MASKED ADVENTURER ALWAYS CARRIES SPARE WEB-FLUID CAPSULES CLIPPED ONTO HIS INGENIOUSLY DESIGNED UTILITY BELT!

BY ADJUSTING THE NOZZLE OF HIS WEB-SHOOTER IN ONE EASY MOTION, SPIDEY CAN EJECT HIS WEB FLUID IN ANY ONE OF THREE DIFFERENT WAYS...

1. AS A THIN, INCREDIBLY STRONG LINE...

2. AS A FINE, QUICK-SPREADING SPRAY...

3. OR AS A THICK, TREMENDOUS-LY ADHESIVE LIQUID....!

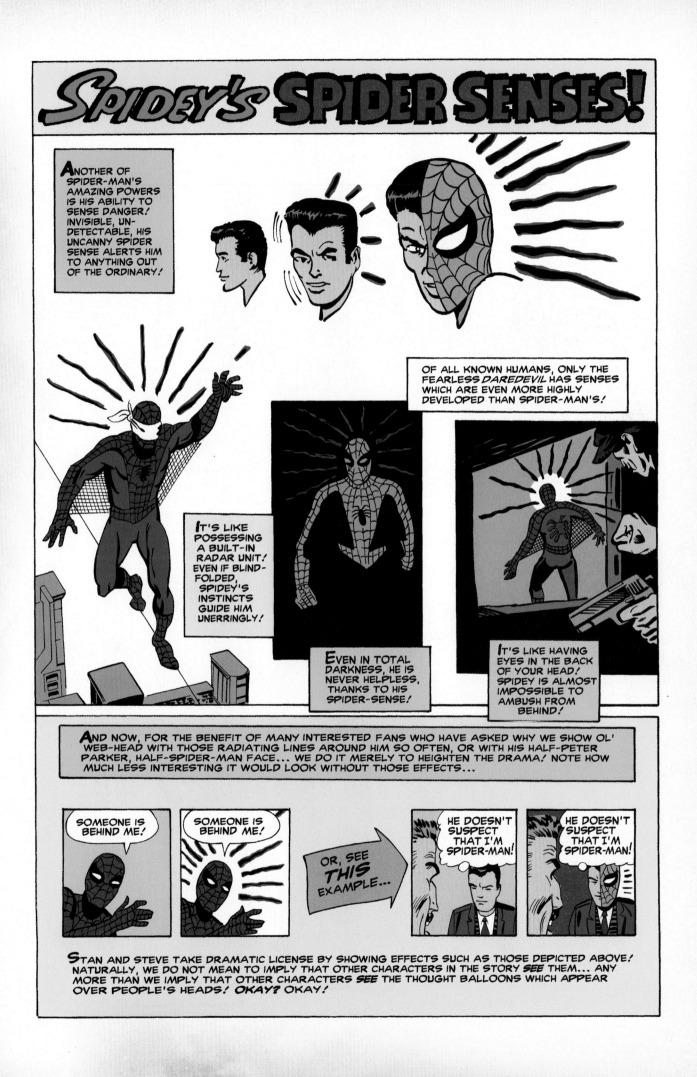

the BURGLAR

FIRST APPEARED IN...

AMAZING FANTASY

15 AUG.

THIS UNNAMED THIEF IS THE MAN RESPONSIBLE FOR SPIDER-MAN'S VOW TO USE HIS GREAT POWERS TO COMBAT CRIME! FOR, IT WAS THIS ARMED THUG WHO CAUSED THE DEATH OF PETER PARKER'S BELOVED UNCLE, BEN PARKER! ONE FATAL, COWARDLY SHOT...ONE MOMENT OF STARK TRAGEDY, AND A LEGEND WAS BORN!

A GALLERY OF SPIDER-MAN'S MOST FAMOUS FOES!

SANDMAN

POSSIBLY ONE OF THE MOST TRULY ORIGINAL, TRULY UNIQUE VILLAINS IN THIS, THE MARVEL AGE OF COMICS!

FIRST APPEARED IN...

4 SEPT.

FLINT MARKO HAD SPENT A LARGE PORTION OF HIS LIFE IN PRISON! A HABITUAL OFFENDER, HE WAS KNOWN AS ONE OF THE MOST INCORRIGIBLE PRISONERS AT MANY OF THE NATION'S MAXIMUM SECURITY JAILS! BUT, ONE NIGHT, DURING AN ATTEMPTED ESCAPE, HE HID ON A BEACH, NEAR THE SCENE OF AN ATOMIC TEST EXPLOSION! THERE, BY SOME INCREDIBLE ACCIDENT, THE MOLECULES OF HIS BODY MERGED WITH THE SAND UNDER HIS FEET, AND HIS BODY TOOK ON THE QUALITIES OF THE SAND ITSELF -- BECOMING VIRTUALLY INDESTRUCTIBLE! TO THIS VERY DAY, SANDMAN IS REGARDED BY PENAL AUTHORITIES AS ALMOST IMPOSSIBLE TO KEEP IMPRISONED!

X-722

The VULTURE

FROM...

the AMAZING SPIDER-MAN

MARVEL COMICS GROUP 12¢

2 MAY

FANDOM WILL NEVER FORGET THE FIRST BATTLE BETWEEN THE VULTURE AND SPIDER-MAN! HIGH ABOVE THE TOWERING SKYSCRAPERS THEY FOUGHT, THE MYSTERIOUS WINGED MENACE, AND THE TEEN-AGE CRIME-FIGHTER WHO HAD NEVER YET BATTLED SO DANGEROUS, SO POWERFUL A FOE!

ACTUALLY, IT WAS IN THIS EPIC BATTLE THAT SPIDER-MAN IS SAID TO HAVE TRULY UNDERGONE HIS BAPTISM OF FIRE!

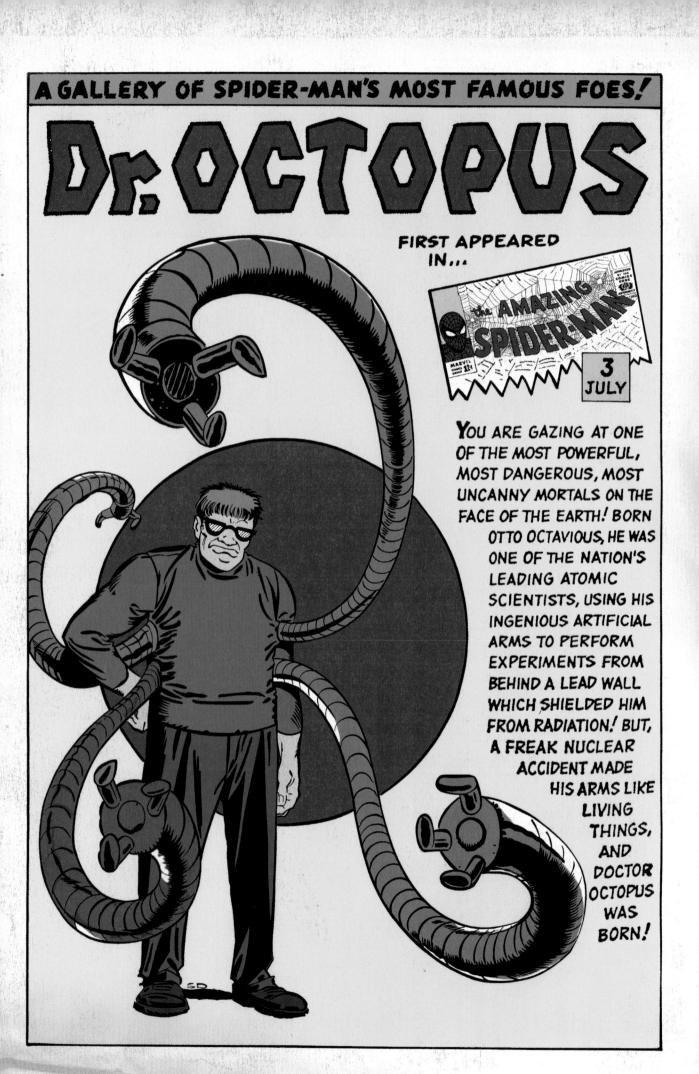